January 2021

SUN	MON	TUE	WED	THUR	FRI	SAT
					1	2
3	4	5	6	7	8	9
10	11	12	13	14	15	16
17	18	19	20	21	22	23
24	25	26	27	28	29	30
31						

December/January

SUNDAY
27

MONDAY
28

TUESDAY
29

WEDNESDAY
30

THURSDAY
31

NEW YEAR'S DAY

FRIDAY
1

SATURDAY
2

January

January 2021

SUN	MON	TUE	WED	THUR	FRI	SAT
					1	2
3	4	5	6	7	8	9
10	11	12	13	14	15	16
17	18	19	20	21	22	23
24	25	26	27	28	29	30
31						

SUNDAY

3

MONDAY

4

TUESDAY

5

WEDNESDAY

◑

6

THURSDAY

7

FRIDAY

8

SATURDAY

9

January

Maine was at the forefront of the ice industry from 1870 to 1890, with ice cut from Maine rivers and lakes sent all around the world. Two thirds of that ice — about 1.5 million tons per year — came from the Kennebec River.

SUNDAY

10

MONDAY

11

TUESDAY

12

●

WEDNESDAY

13

THURSDAY

14

FRIDAY

15

SATURDAY

16

Gift shop in an 1889 livery stable, Cape Porpoise. By Robert A. Dennis.

January 2021

SUN	MON	TUE	WED	THUR	FRI	SAT
					1	2
3	4	5	6	7	8	9
10	11	12	13	14	15	16
17	18	19	20	21	22	23
24	25	26	27	28	29	30
31						

January

SUNDAY

17

MARTIN LUTHER KING JR. DAY

MONDAY

18

TUESDAY

19

◐

WEDNESDAY

20

THURSDAY

21

FRIDAY

22

SATURDAY

23

January

January 2021

SUN	MON	TUE	WED	THUR	FRI	SAT
					1	2
3	4	5	6	7	8	9
10	11	12	13	14	15	16
17	18	19	20	21	22	23
24	25	26	27	28	29	30
31						

SUNDAY

24

MONDAY

25

TUESDAY

26

WEDNESDAY

27

THURSDAY   ○

28

FRIDAY

29

SATURDAY

30

February 2021

SUN	MON	TUE	WED	THUR	FRI	SAT
	1	2	3	4	5	6
7	8	9	10	11	12	13
14	15	16	17	18	19	20
21	22	23	24	25	26	27
28						

January/February

On February 2, 1915, imperial German spy Werner Horn tried, but failed, to blow up the St. Croix–Vanceboro Railway Bridge. Due to ill health, he was deported after serving only one year of his 10-year sentence.

SUNDAY

31

MONDAY

1

GROUNDHOG DAY

TUESDAY

2

WEDNESDAY

3

◑

THURSDAY

4

FRIDAY

5

SATURDAY

6

100 Mile Wilderness. By Greta Rybus.

February 2021

SUN	MON	TUE	WED	THUR	FRI	SAT
	1	2	3	4	5	6
7	8	9	10	11	12	13
14	15	16	17	18	19	20
21	22	23	24	25	26	27
28						

February

SUNDAY

7

MONDAY

8

TUESDAY

9

WEDNESDAY

10

THURSDAY

11

FRIDAY

12

SATURDAY

13

February

February 2021

SUN	MON	TUE	WED	THUR	FRI	SAT
	1	2	3	4	5	6
7	8	9	10	11	12	13
14	15	16	17	18	19	20
21	22	23	24	25	26	27
28						

SUNDAY   VALENTINE'S DAY

14

MONDAY   PRESIDENTS' DAY

15

TUESDAY

16

WEDNESDAY   ASH WEDNESDAY

17

THURSDAY

18

FRIDAY   ◑

19

SATURDAY

20

February

By the late 1800s, the fisher cat had been extirpated in the Northeast except for Maine. It has since made a comeback and can be found throughout New England. The fisher cat doesn't fish, and it's not a cat (it's a weasel).

SUNDAY
21

MONDAY
22

TUESDAY
23

WEDNESDAY
24

THURSDAY
25

FRIDAY
26

○

SATURDAY
27

Sparhawk Mill, Yarmouth. By Benjamin Williamson.

March 2021

SUN	MON	TUE	WED	THUR	FRI	SAT
	1	2	3	4	5	6
7	8	9	10	11	12	13
14	15	16	17	18	19	20
21	22	23	24	25	26	27
28	29	30	31			

SUNDAY

28

MONDAY

1

TUESDAY

2

WEDNESDAY

3

THURSDAY

4

FRIDAY

5

SATURDAY

6

March

March 2021

SUN	MON	TUE	WED	THUR	FRI	SAT
	1	2	3	4	5	6
7	8	9	10	11	12	13
14	15	16	17	18	19	20
21	22	23	24	25	26	27
28	29	30	31			

SUNDAY

7

MONDAY

8

TUESDAY

9

WEDNESDAY

10

THURSDAY

11

FRIDAY

12

SATURDAY

13

March

Portland was the first capital of Maine, but in
1832, the designation was changed to Augusta
because of its more central location.

DAYLIGHT SAVING TIME BEGINS

14

MONDAY

15

TUESDAY

16

ST. PATRICK'S DAY

WEDNESDAY

17

THURSDAY

18

FRIDAY

19

VERNAL EQUINOX

SATURDAY

20

Lobster buoys on a Camden lake camp. By Sarah Rice.

March 2021

SUN	MON	TUE	WED	THUR	FRI	SAT
	1	2	3	4	5	6
7	8	9	10	11	12	13
14	15	16	17	18	19	20
21	22	23	24	25	26	27
28	29	30	31			

March

SUNDAY

21

MONDAY

22

TUESDAY

23

WEDNESDAY

24

THURSDAY

25

FRIDAY

26

PASSOVER BEGINS

SATURDAY

27

March/April

April 2021

SUN	MON	TUE	WED	THUR	FRI	SAT
				1	2	3
4	5	6	7	8	9	10
11	12	13	14	15	16	17
18	19	20	21	22	23	24
25	26	27	28	29	30	

SUNDAY   PALM SUNDAY

28   ○

MONDAY

29

TUESDAY

30

WEDNESDAY

31

THURSDAY   APRIL FOOL'S DAY

1

FRIDAY   GOOD FRIDAY

2

SATURDAY   PASSOVER ENDS

3

April

Suffragist Maud Wood Park, who lived in Cape Elizabeth
during her retirement years, became the first president of the
newly formed League of Women Voters in 1920.

EASTER SUNDAY

SUNDAY

4

MONDAY

5

TUESDAY

6

WEDNESDAY

7

THURSDAY

8

FRIDAY

9

SATURDAY

10

Bunchberry, also known as creeping dogwood. By Colleen Miniuk-Sperry.

April 2021

SUN	MON	TUE	WED	THUR	FRI	SAT
				1	2	3
4	5	6	7	8	9	10
11	12	13	14	15	16	17
18	19	20	21	22	23	24
25	26	27	28	29	30	

April

●   SUNDAY

11

MONDAY

12

RAMADAN BEGINS   TUESDAY

13

WEDNESDAY

14

TAX DAY   THURSDAY

15

FRIDAY

16

SATURDAY

17

April

April 2021

SUN	MON	TUE	WED	THUR	FRI	SAT
				1	2	3
4	5	6	7	8	9	10
11	12	13	14	15	16	17
18	19	20	21	22	23	24
25	26	27	28	29	30	

SUNDAY

18

MONDAY   PATRIOT'S DAY

19

TUESDAY   ◑

20

WEDNESDAY

21

THURSDAY

22

FRIDAY

23

SATURDAY

24

April/May

Hiram Maxim, who was born in Sangerville, invented the first portable fully automatic machine gun and developed and installed the first electric lights in a New York City building.

SUNDAY

25

MONDAY

○

26

TUESDAY

27

WEDNESDAY

28

THURSDAY

29

FRIDAY

30

SATURDAY

1

Dike Brook flowing into Grand Marsh Bay, Gouldsboro. By Paul Rezendes.

Get your free trial issue

Don't miss out!

We'd like to give you a copy of *Down East* so you can see for yourself the sort of engaging stories and gorgeous photography you'll get in every issue.

See reverse side for details

To get your free copy of *Down East*, fill out the form below.

Get Your Free Trial Issue

Your Name

Address

City/State/ZIP

☑ YES - Send my free trial issue today!

Email address

M2AME1

We'll enter your subscription for a full year (11 additional issues, for a total of 12) for just $28. If, after previewing your free trial issue, you do not wish to subscribe, write "cancel" across the invoice, return it, and owe nothing. *The free issue is yours to keep regardless.*

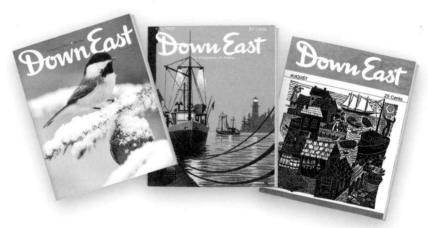

The Magazine of Maine for more than 60 years.

ORDER ONLINE
downeast.com/trial21

ORDER BY PHONE:
800-727-7422

ORDER BY MAIL
Send this completed form to:
Down East
PO Box 679
Camden, ME 04843-0679

May 2021

SUN	MON	TUE	WED	THUR	FRI	SAT
						1
2	3	4	5	6	7	8
9	10	11	12	13	14	15
16	17	18	19	20	21	22
23	24	25	26	27	28	29
30	31					

May

SUNDAY

2

MONDAY

3

TUESDAY

4

CINCO DE MAYO

WEDNESDAY

5

THURSDAY

6

FRIDAY

7

SATURDAY

8

May

May 2021

SUN	MON	TUE	WED	THUR	FRI	SAT
						1
2	3	4	5	6	7	8
9	10	11	12	13	14	15
16	17	18	19	20	21	22
23	24	25	26	27	28	29
30	31					

SUNDAY   MOTHER'S DAY

9

MONDAY

10

TUESDAY   RAMADAN ENDS
                                                                    ●

11

WEDNESDAY

12

THURSDAY

13

FRIDAY

14

SATURDAY

15

May

A lobster car isn't a car at all. It's a raft in which lobsters are stored.

SUNDAY

16

MONDAY

17

TUESDAY

18

WEDNESDAY

19

THURSDAY

20

FRIDAY

21

SATURDAY

22

Pennesseewassee Lake, Norway. By Jeremy Garretson.

May 2021

SUN	MON	TUE	WED	THUR	FRI	SAT
						1
2	3	4	5	6	7	8
9	10	11	12	13	14	15
16	17	18	19	20	21	22
23	24	25	26	27	28	29
30	31					

May

SUNDAY
23

MONDAY
24

TUESDAY
25

○ WEDNESDAY
26

THURSDAY
27

FRIDAY
28

SATURDAY
29

May/June

June 2021

SUN	MON	TUE	WED	THUR	FRI	SAT
		1	2	3	4	5
6	7	8	9	10	11	12
13	14	15	16	17	18	19
20	21	22	23	24	25	26
27	28	29	30			

SUNDAY

30

MONDAY   MEMORIAL DAY

31

TUESDAY

1

WEDNESDAY   ◗

2

THURSDAY

3

FRIDAY

4

SATURDAY

5

June

Pond Island was the boyhood home of Robert Peter Tristram
Coffin and the scene of his book *The Lost Paradise*.

SUNDAY

6

MONDAY

7

TUESDAY

8

WEDNESDAY

9

●

THURSDAY

10

FRIDAY

11

SATURDAY

12

Monhegan Island Light. By Benjamin Williamson.

June 2021

SUN	MON	TUE	WED	THUR	FRI	SAT
		1	2	3	4	5
6	7	8	9	10	11	12
13	14	15	16	17	18	19
20	21	22	23	24	25	26
27	28	29	30			

June

SUNDAY

13

FLAG DAY

MONDAY

14

TUESDAY

15

WEDNESDAY

16

◑ THURSDAY

17

FRIDAY

18

SATURDAY

19

June

June 2021

SUN	MON	TUE	WED	THUR	FRI	SAT
		1	2	3	4	5
6	7	8	9	10	11	12
13	14	15	16	17	18	19
20	21	22	23	24	25	26
27	28	29	30			

SUNDAY   FATHER'S DAY

20

MONDAY   SUMMER SOLSTICE

21

TUESDAY

22

WEDNESDAY

23

THURSDAY   ○

24

FRIDAY

25

SATURDAY

26

July 2021

SUN	MON	TUE	WED	THUR	FRI	SAT
				1	2	3
4	5	6	7	8	9	10
11	12	13	14	15	16	17
18	19	20	21	22	23	24
25	26	27	28	29	30	31

June/July

An unknown Confederate soldier is buried in Gray
because his body was mistakenly sent to Maine in the
casket meant for Union soldier Charles H. Colley.

SUNDAY

27

MONDAY

28

TUESDAY

29

WEDNESDAY

30

THURSDAY

1

FRIDAY

2

SATURDAY

3

Pepperrell Cove, Kittery. By Harry Lichtman.

July 2021

SUN	MON	TUE	WED	THUR	FRI	SAT
				1	2	3
4	5	6	7	8	9	10
11	12	13	14	15	16	17
18	19	20	21	22	23	24
25	26	27	28	29	30	31

July

INDEPENDENCE DAY

SUNDAY

4

INDEPENDENCE DAY OBSERVED

MONDAY

5

TUESDAY

6

WEDNESDAY

7

THURSDAY

8

●

FRIDAY

9

SATURDAY

10

July

July 2021

SUN	MON	TUE	WED	THUR	FRI	SAT
				1	2	3
4	5	6	7	8	9	10
11	12	13	14	15	16	17
18	19	20	21	22	23	24
25	26	27	28	29	30	31

SUNDAY

11

MONDAY

12

TUESDAY

13

WEDNESDAY

14

THURSDAY

15

FRIDAY

16

SATURDAY

17

July

During the Civil War, drafted Mainers could
avoid serving by hiring a substitute for $300.

SUNDAY

18

MONDAY

19

TUESDAY

20

WEDNESDAY

21

THURSDAY

22

○   FRIDAY

23

SATURDAY

24

View from Lookout Point, Harpswell. By Benjamin Williamson.

SUN	MON	TUE	WED	THUR	FRI	SAT
				1	2	3
4	5	6	7	8	9	10
11	12	13	14	15	16	17
18	19	20	21	22	23	24
25	26	27	28	29	30	31

July

SUNDAY

25

MONDAY

26

TUESDAY

27

WEDNESDAY

28

THURSDAY

29

FRIDAY

30

SATURDAY

31

August

August 2021

SUN	MON	TUE	WED	THUR	FRI	SAT
1	2	3	4	5	6	7
8	9	10	11	12	13	14
15	16	17	18	19	20	21
22	23	24	25	26	27	28
29	30	31				

SUNDAY

1

MONDAY

2

TUESDAY

3

WEDNESDAY

4

THURSDAY

5

FRIDAY

6

SATURDAY

7

August

The remains of the villages of Dead River and Flagstaff rest on the floor of Flagstaff Lake, which was created in 1949 by the construction of the Long Falls Dam.

SUNDAY

8

MONDAY

9

TUESDAY

10

WEDNESDAY

11

THURSDAY

12

FRIDAY

13

SATURDAY

14

Geraniums, Hancock. By Nicole Wolf.

August 2021

SUN	MON	TUE	WED	THUR	FRI	SAT
1	2	3	4	5	6	7
8	9	10	11	12	13	14
15	16	17	18	19	20	21
22	23	24	25	26	27	28
29	30	31				

August

SUNDAY

15

MONDAY

16

TUESDAY

17

WEDNESDAY

18

THURSDAY

19

FRIDAY

20

SATURDAY

21

August

August 2021

SUN	MON	TUE	WED	THUR	FRI	SAT
1	2	3	4	5	6	7
8	9	10	11	12	13	14
15	16	17	18	19	20	21
22	23	24	25	26	27	28
29	30	31				

SUNDAY ○

22

MONDAY

23

TUESDAY

24

WEDNESDAY

25

THURSDAY

26

FRIDAY

27

SATURDAY

28

September 2021

SUN	MON	TUE	WED	THUR	FRI	SAT
			1	2	3	4
5	6	7	8	9	10	11
12	13	14	15	16	17	18
19	20	21	22	23	24	25
26	27	28	29	30		

August/September

The University of Maine Farmington is affectionately known "the Farm."

SUNDAY

29

MONDAY

30

TUESDAY

31

WEDNESDAY

1

THURSDAY

2

FRIDAY

3

SATURDAY

4

Monarch on verbena, York. By Nicole Wolf.

Order your 2022 *Down East* calendars today!

Each includes holidays, moon phases, and tide tables, and features extraordinary color photos.

Your Name

Address

City/State/ZIP

Daytime Phone   E-mail Address

CALENDARS SHIPPED TO ADDRESS ABOVE

_____ 2022 *Down East* Maine Wall Calendars	$14.99 each	$ _____
_____ 2022 *Down East* Maine Engagement Calendars	$14.99 each	$ _____
_____ 2022 Acadia Wall Calendars	$14.99 each	$ _____
_____ 2022 Maine Coon Cat Wall Calendars	$14.99 each	$ _____
_____ 2022 Maine Lighthouses Wall Calendars	$14.99 each	$ _____
_____ 2022 Sea Glass Wall Calendars	$14.99 each	$ _____
_____ 2022 Maine Lobstering Wall Calendars	$14.99 each	$ _____

GIFT CALENDARS (from other side)

_____ 2022 *Down East* Maine Wall Calendars	$14.99 each	$ _____
_____ 2022 *Down East* Maine Engagement Calendars	$14.99 each	$ _____
_____ 2022 Acadia Wall Calendars	$14.99 each	$ _____
_____ 2022 Maine Coon Cat Wall Calendars	$14.99 each	$ _____
_____ 2022 Maine Lighthouses Wall Calendars	$14.99 each	$ _____
_____ 2022 Sea Glass Wall Calendars	$14.99 each	$ _____
_____ 2022 Maine Lobstering Wall Calendars	$14.99 each	$ _____

Add 5.5% state sales tax on orders sent to Maine addresses: $ _____

Shipping & handling (U.S. addresses only) $ ____**FREE!***____

FREE shipping when you place your order by mail with this form only.

Foreign addresses: add $15.00 per calendar (1st class shipping) (except APO and FPO) $ _____

GRAND TOTAL $ _____

Make checks payable to *Down East*. Foreign and Canadian orders: pay in U.S. dollars by international money order. For credit card payments, please complete the information below:

❏ Visa   ❏ MasterCard   ❏ American Express   ❏ Discover

Card # _____ Expiration Date _____

Signature _____ Security Code _____

ORDER ONLINE
downeast.com/store

ORDER BY PHONE
800-685-7962

E-MAIL
products@downeast.com

ORDER BY MAIL
send this completed form to:
Down East
PO Box 679
Camden, ME 04843-0679

LET US MAIL YOUR GIFT!
We can mail your gift calendars directly to friends, relatives, and business associates. **List names and addresses on the back of this page.** Place your gift orders early; allow 30 days for delivery.

CAL21ME

If you wish to order gift calendars, use the spaces below.

Please be sure that your own name and address are listed on the other side of this form.

Send Gift Calendars To:

Recipient Name

Address

City/State/ZIP

❑ *Down East* **Maine Wall Calendar**
❑ *Down East* **Maine Engagement Calendar**
❑ **Acadia Wall Calendar**
❑ **Maine Lobstering Wall Calendar**

❑ **Maine Coon Cat Wall Calendar**
❑ **Maine Lighthouses Wall Calendar**
❑ **Sea Glass Wall Calendar**

Gift Card: From _____

❑ *Ship Now*　　　　❑ *Ship for Christmas*

Recipient Name

Address

City/State/ZIP

❑ *Down East* **Maine Wall Calendar**
❑ *Down East* **Maine Engagement Calendar**
❑ **Acadia Wall Calendar**
❑ **Maine Lobstering Wall Calendar**

❑ **Maine Coon Cat Wall Calendar**
❑ **Maine Lighthouses Wall Calendar**
❑ **Sea Glass Wall Calendar**

Gift Card: From _____

❑ *Ship Now*　　　　❑ *Ship for Christmas*

Recipient Name

Address

City/State/ZIP

❑ *Down East* **Maine Wall Calendar**
❑ *Down East* **Maine Engagement Calendar**
❑ **Acadia Wall Calendar**
❑ **Maine Lobstering Wall Calendar**

❑ **Maine Coon Cat Wall Calendar**
❑ **Maine Lighthouses Wall Calendar**
❑ **Sea Glass Wall Calendar**

Gift Card: From _____

❑ *Ship Now*　　　　❑ *Ship for Christmas*

September 2021

SUN	MON	TUE	WED	THUR	FRI	SAT
			1	2	3	4
5	6	7	8	9	10	11
12	13	14	15	16	17	18
19	20	21	22	23	24	25
26	27	28	29	30		

September

SUNDAY

5

LABOR DAY

●

MONDAY

6

ROSH HASHANAH

TUESDAY

7

WEDNESDAY

8

THURSDAY

9

FRIDAY

10

SATURDAY

11

September

September 2021

SUN	MON	TUE	WED	THUR	FRI	SAT
			1	2	3	4
5	6	7	8	9	10	11
12	13	14	15	16	17	18
19	20	21	22	23	24	25
26	27	28	29	30		

SUNDAY

12

MONDAY ◐

13

TUESDAY

14

WEDNESDAY

15

THURSDAY   YOM KIPPUR

16

FRIDAY

17

SATURDAY

18

September

In the 18th century, codfish were cured in piles of salt, marsh hay, eel grass, and manure. The result, called dunfish, was considered a delicacy in the royal courts of Europe.

SUNDAY

19

○

MONDAY

20

TUESDAY

21

AUTUMNAL EQUINOX

WEDNESDAY

22

THURSDAY

23

FRIDAY

24

SATURDAY

25

Foliage on Flagstaff Lake. By Benjamin Williamson.

September 2021

SUN	MON	TUE	WED	THUR	FRI	SAT
			1	2	3	4
5	6	7	8	9	10	11
12	13	14	15	16	17	18
19	20	21	22	23	24	25
26	27	28	29	30		

September/October

SUNDAY

26

MONDAY

27

TUESDAY

28

WEDNESDAY

29

THURSDAY

30

FRIDAY

1

SATURDAY

2

October

October 2021

SUN	MON	TUE	WED	THUR	FRI	SAT
					1	2
3	4	5	6	7	8	9
10	11	12	13	14	15	16
17	18	19	20	21	22	23
24	25	26	27	28	29	30
31						

SUNDAY

3

MONDAY

4

TUESDAY

5

WEDNESDAY   ●

6

THURSDAY

7

FRIDAY

8

SATURDAY

9

October

Depending on the source, Mysterious Billy, the first welterweight boxing champion of the world, was born in Eastport, Maine; Little River, Nova Scotia; or St. John, New Brunswick. Smith himself once told a newspaper reporter he was born in St. Louis, Missouri. And his real name wasn't Billy. It was Amos Smith.

SUNDAY

10

INDIGENOUS PEOPLES' DAY / COLUMBUS DAY

MONDAY

11

TUESDAY

12

WEDNESDAY

13

THURSDAY

14

FRIDAY

15

SATURDAY

16

Chickadee, the Maine state bird. By Mark J. Bilak.

October 2021

SUN	MON	TUE	WED	THUR	FRI	SAT
					1	2
3	4	5	6	7	8	9
10	11	12	13	14	15	16
17	18	19	20	21	22	23
24	25	26	27	28	29	30
31						

October

SUNDAY

17

MONDAY

18

TUESDAY

19

○

WEDNESDAY

20

THURSDAY

21

FRIDAY

22

SATURDAY

23

October

October 2021

SUN	MON	TUE	WED	THUR	FRI	SAT
					1	2
3	4	5	6	7	8	9
10	11	12	13	14	15	16
17	18	19	20	21	22	23
24	25	26	27	28	29	30
31						

SUNDAY

24

MONDAY

25

TUESDAY

26

WEDNESDAY

27

THURSDAY

28

FRIDAY

29

SATURDAY

30

The line that connects the lobster trap to the buoy is called a wrap.

November 2021

SUN	MON	TUE	WED	THUR	FRI	SAT
	1	2	3	4	5	6
7	8	9	10	11	12	13
14	15	16	17	18	19	20
21	22	23	24	25	26	27
28	29	30				

HALLOWEEN

SUNDAY

31

MONDAY

1

TUESDAY

2

WEDNESDAY

3

THURSDAY

4

FRIDAY

5

SATURDAY

6

Lazy Tom Stream, Piscataquis County. By Paul Rezendes.

November 2021

SUN	MON	TUE	WED	THUR	FRI	SAT
	1	2	3	4	5	6
7	8	9	10	11	12	13
14	15	16	17	18	19	20
21	22	23	24	25	26	27
28	29	30				

November

DAYLIGHT SAVING TIME ENDS

SUNDAY

7

MONDAY

8

TUESDAY

9

WEDNESDAY

10

VETERANS DAY

◑

THURSDAY

11

FRIDAY

12

SATURDAY

13

November

November 2021

SUN	MON	TUE	WED	THUR	FRI	SAT
	1	2	3	4	5	6
7	8	9	10	11	12	13
14	15	16	17	18	19	20
21	22	23	24	25	26	27
28	29	30				

SUNDAY

14

MONDAY

15

TUESDAY

16

WEDNESDAY

17

THURSDAY

18

FRIDAY   ○

19

SATURDAY

20

November

The first fire lookout station in Maine, and possibly the nation, was built atop Big Moose Mountain in 1905.

SUNDAY

21

MONDAY

22

TUESDAY

23

WEDNESDAY

24

THANKSGIVING

THURSDAY

25

FRIDAY

26

◗

SATURDAY

27

Maple leaves and birch bark in western Maine. By Benjamin Williamson.

December 2021

SUN	MON	TUE	WED	THUR	FRI	SAT
			1	2	3	4
5	6	7	8	9	10	11
12	13	14	15	16	17	18
19	20	21	22	23	24	25
26	27	28	29	30	31	

SUNDAY

28

MONDAY

HANUKKAH BEGINS

29

TUESDAY

30

WEDNESDAY

1

THURSDAY

2

FRIDAY

3

●

SATURDAY

4

December

December 2021

SUN	MON	TUE	WED	THUR	FRI	SAT
			1	2	3	4
5	6	7	8	9	10	11
12	13	14	15	16	17	18
19	20	21	22	23	24	25
26	27	28	29	30	31	

SUNDAY

5

MONDAY   HANUKKAH ENDS

6

TUESDAY   PEARL HARBOR DAY

7

WEDNESDAY

8

THURSDAY

9

FRIDAY   ◖

10

SATURDAY

11

December

Bath is the only city in Sagadahoc County. The City of Ships has a little over 8,300 residents.

SUNDAY
12

MONDAY
13

TUESDAY
14

WEDNESDAY
15

THURSDAY
16

FRIDAY
17

○

SATURDAY
18

A classic New England Cape. By Benjamin Williamson.

December 2021

SUN	MON	TUE	WED	THUR	FRI	SAT
			1	2	3	4
5	6	7	8	9	10	11
12	13	14	15	16	17	18
19	20	21	22	23	24	25
26	27	28	29	30	31	

December

SUNDAY

19

MONDAY

20

WINTER SOLSTICE

TUESDAY

21

WEDNESDAY

22

THURSDAY

23

CHRISTMAS EVE

FRIDAY

24

CHRISTMAS DAY

SATURDAY

25

December/January

December 2021

SUN	MON	TUE	WED	THUR	FRI	SAT
			1	2	3	4
5	6	7	8	9	10	11
12	13	14	15	16	17	18
19	20	21	22	23	24	25
26	27	28	29	30	31	

SUNDAY   KWANZAA BEGINS

26   ◑

MONDAY

27

TUESDAY

28

WEDNESDAY

29

THURSDAY

30

FRIDAY   NEW YEAR'S EVE

31

SATURDAY

1

2022

at a glance

January 2022

SUN	MON	TUE	WED	THUR	FRI	SAT
						1
2	3	4	5	6	7	8
9	10	11	12	13	14	15
16	17	18	19	20	21	22
23	24	25	26	27	28	29
30	31					

February 2022

SUN	MON	TUE	WED	THUR	FRI	SAT
		1	2	3	4	5
6	7	8	9	10	11	12
13	14	15	16	17	18	19
20	21	22	23	24	25	26
27	28					

March 2022

SUN	MON	TUE	WED	THUR	FRI	SAT
		1	2	3	4	5
6	7	8	9	10	11	12
13	14	15	16	17	18	19
20	21	22	23	24	25	26
27	28	29	30	31		

April 2022

SUN	MON	TUE	WED	THUR	FRI	SAT
					1	2
3	4	5	6	7	8	9
10	11	12	13	14	15	16
17	18	19	20	21	22	23
24	25	26	27	28	29	30

May 2022

SUN	MON	TUE	WED	THUR	FRI	SAT
1	2	3	4	5	6	7
8	9	10	11	12	13	14
15	16	17	18	19	20	21
22	23	24	25	26	27	28
29	30	31				

June 2022

SUN	MON	TUE	WED	THUR	FRI	SAT
			1	2	3	4
5	6	7	8	9	10	11
12	13	14	15	16	17	18
19	20	21	22	23	24	25
26	27	28	29	30		

July 2022

SUN	MON	TUE	WED	THUR	FRI	SAT
					1	2
3	4	5	6	7	8	9
10	11	12	13	14	15	16
17	18	19	20	21	22	23
24	25	26	27	28	29	30
31						

August 2022

SUN	MON	TUE	WED	THUR	FRI	SAT
	1	2	3	4	5	6
7	8	9	10	11	12	13
14	15	16	17	18	19	20
21	22	23	24	25	26	27
28	29	30	31			

September 2022

SUN	MON	TUE	WED	THUR	FRI	SAT
				1	2	3
4	5	6	7	8	9	10
11	12	13	14	15	16	17
18	19	20	21	22	23	24
25	26	27	28	29	30	

October 2022

SUN	MON	TUE	WED	THUR	FRI	SAT
						1
2	3	4	5	6	7	8
9	10	11	12	13	14	15
16	17	18	19	20	21	22
23	24	25	26	27	28	29
30	31					

November 2022

SUN	MON	TUE	WED	THUR	FRI	SAT
		1	2	3	4	5
6	7	8	9	10	11	12
13	14	15	16	17	18	19
20	21	22	23	24	25	26
27	28	29	30			

December 2022

SUN	MON	TUE	WED	THUR	FRI	SAT
				1	2	3
4	5	6	7	8	9	10
11	12	13	14	15	16	17
18	19	20	21	22	23	24
25	26	27	28	29	30	31

2021
tides

DAY	JANUARY A.M.	JANUARY P.M.	FEBRUARY A.M.	FEBRUARY P.M.	MARCH A.M.	MARCH P.M.	APRIL A.M.	APRIL P.M.	MAY A.M.	MAY P.M.	JUNE A.M.	JUNE P.M.
1	12:18	12:17	1:14	1:27	12:05	12:23	2:09	2:47	2:43	3:32	4:28	5:19
2	12:57	12:59	1:59	2:16	12:48	1:10	3:01	3:44	3:42	4:36	5:31	6:18
3	1:39	1:44	2:47	3:11	1:33	2:01	3:58	4:48	4:47	5:41	6:33	7:15
4	2:24	2:34	3:41	4:12	2:22	2:57	5:02	5:56	5:54	6:47	7:34	8:09
5	3:14	3:29	4:38	5:17	3:17	3:59	6:11	7:06	7:02	7:50	8:33	8:58
6	4:07	4:29	5:40	6:28	4:18	5:06	7:23	8:14	8:07	8:47	9:25	9:42
7	5:03	5:33	6:47	7:38	5:24	6:18	8:31	9:14	9:06	9:36	10:13	10:23
8	6:02	6:40	7:53	8:41	6:36	7:29	9:30	10:05	9:57	10:19	10:57	11:01
9	7:04	7:47	8:53	9:37	7:44	8:31	10:21	10:49	10:43	10:57	11:39	11:39
10	8:03	8:48	9:47	10:28	8:45	9:25	11:07	11:29	11:25	11:34		12:19
11	9:00	9:45	10:38	11:15	9:38	10:13	11:49			12:04	12:15	12:57
12	9:54	10:39	11:25	11:58	10:26	10:55	12:05	12:28	12:08	12:42	12:51	1:35
13	10:47	11:30		12:08	11:09	11:34	12:39	1:04	12:41	1:19	1:28	2:12
14	11:37		12:39	12:50		12:49	1:11	1:40	1:15	1:55	2:06	2:52
15	12:18	12:25	1:17	1:31	1:10	1:27	1:43	2:17	1:50	2:33	2:48	3:34
16	1:04	1:12	1:56	2:13	1:44	2:04	2:17	2:56	2:27	3:14	3:34	4:20
17	1:50	1:59	2:36	2:59	2:17	2:42	2:55	3:38	3:10	3:59	4:25	5:09
18	2:37	2:48	3:19	3:48	2:53	3:23	3:38	4:26	3:57	4:49	5:19	6:00
19	3:24	3:40	4:05	4:42	3:31	4:09	4:27	5:19	4:50	5:40	6:17	6:53
20	4:12	4:34	4:56	5:40	4:16	4:59	5:22	6:15	5:47	6:34	7:19	7:49
21	5:02	5:31	5:52	6:43	5:06	5:55	6:21	7:13	6:46	7:28	8:22	8:45
22	5:54	6:30	6:52	7:42	6:02	6:56	7:23	8:09	7:48	8:22	9:24	9:40
23	6:47	7:29	7:49	8:33	7:04	7:57	8:23	9:00	8:48	9:14	10:22	10:34
24	7:40	8:22	8:39	9:19	8:06	8:52	9:19	9:48	9:45	10:04	11:19	11:29
25	8:28	9:10	9:25	10:02	9:02	9:41	10:12	10:35	10:40	10:54		12:16
26	9:13	9:53	10:10	10:43	9:53	10:25	11:03	11:21	11:35	11:46	12:24	1:10
27	9:55	10:34	10:54	11:24	10:41	11:09	11:54			12:30	1:18	2:04
28	10:36	11:14	11:38		11:28	11:52	12:09	12:46	12:38	1:25	2:11	2:58
29	11:17	11:53				12:16	12:58	1:39	1:32	2:20	3:06	3:53
30	11:58				12:36	1:04	1:49	2:33	2:27	3:18	4:03	4:47
31	12:33	12:41			1:22	1:54			3:26	4:18		

TIMES OF HIGH WATER FOR PORTLAND, MAINE

Corrected for Daylight Saving Time, which begins March 14 and ends November 7.

For Rockland, subtract 16 minutes. For Bar Harbor, subtract 22 minutes.